SURPRISE!

You may be reading the wrong way!

It's true: In keeping with the original Japanese comic format, this book reads from right to left—so action, sound effects, and word balloons are completely reversed. This preserves the orientation of the original artwork—plus, it's fun! Check out the diagram shown here to get the hang of things, and then turn to the other side of the book to get started!

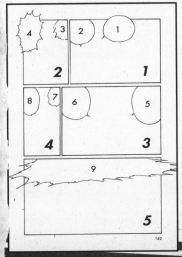

VIZMANGA
Read manga anytime, anywhere!

From our newest hit series to the classics you know and love, the best manga in the world is now available digitally. Buy a volume* of digital manga for your:

- iOS device (**iPad®**, **iPhone®**, **iPod® touch**) through the **VIZ Manga app**

- Android-powered device (**phone or tablet**) with a browser by visiting **VIZManga.com**

- **Mac or PC computer** by visiting **VIZManga.com**

VIZ Digital has loads to offer:

- 500+ ready-to-read volumes
- New volumes each week
- FREE previews
- Access on multiple devices! Create a log-in through the app so you buy a book once, and read it on your device of choice

To learn more, visit **www.viz.com/apps**

* Some series may not be available for multiple devices.
  Check the app on your device to find out what's available.

Aiwo Utayori Oreni Oborero! Volume 1 © Mayu SHINJO 2010
DEATH NOTE © 2003 by Tsugumi Ohba, Takeshi Obata/SHUEISHA Inc.
NURARIHYON NO MAGO © 2008 by Hiroshi Shiibashi/SHUEISHA Inc.

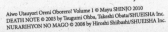

SKIP·BEAT!
Vol. 15
Shojo Beat Edition

STORY AND ART BY YOSHIKI NAKAMURA

English Translation & Adaptation/Tomo Kimura
Touch-up Art & Lettering/Sabrina Heep
Cover Design/Yukiko Whitley
Interior Design/Izumi Evers
Editor/Pancha Diaz

Skip-Beat! by Yoshiki Nakamura © Yoshiki Nakamura 2006
All rights reserved. First published in Japan in 2007 by HAKUSENSHA, Inc., Tokyo.
English language translation rights arranged with HAKUSENSHA, Inc., Tokyo.

Printed in Canada

Published by VIZ Media, LLC
P.O. Box 77010
San Francisco, CA 94107

10 9 8 7 6 5 4 3 2
First printing, November 2008
Second printing, November 2012

www.viz.com

www.shojobeat.com

Yoshiki Nakamura is originally from Tokushima prefecture. She started drawing manga in elementary school, which eventually led to her 1993 debut of *Yume de Au yori Suteki* (Better than Seeing in a Dream) in *Hana to Yume* magazine. Her other works include the basketball series *Saint Love*, *MVP wa Yuzurenai* (Can't Give Up MVP), *Blue Wars*, and *Tokyo Crazy Paradise*, a series about a female bodyguard in 2020 Tokyo.

Skip-Beat! End Notes
Everyone knows how to be a fan, but sometimes cool things
from other cultures need a little help crossing the language barrier.

Page 7, panel 2: Public baths
In Japan, public baths are not just found in resort settings. They are often used on a regular basis by people whose living situations do not include a bathtub, or by people who enjoy the communal aspect. Most public baths include sex-segregated pools inside the larger bath complex, although there are some bathhouses that have mixed bathing.

Page 21, panel 5: Yukata
Lightweight summer garments often worn by women and children to festivals and fireworks displays. *Yukata* are also provided at traditional Japanese inns that include a hot spring for customers to wear after bathing. The word literally means "bath clothes."

Page 50, panel 3: Soft and firm tofu
Kinugoshi, or silken tofu, is a fine-grained tofu, with the softest texture. *Momen*, or cotton tofu, has a firmer texture and is made by pressing the excess liquid out of the tofu.

Page 76, panel 5: Visual kei
A style of Japanese rock that incorporates eccentric and fantastical costumes, hairstyles, and make-up.

Page 137, panel 3: Crying yourself to sleep
The Japanese is *nakineiri*, and it means to let a matter drop without protesting.

Page 158, panel 5: Haigorei
Haigorei means "spirits behind your back," and usually refers to evil spirits that possess humans, although they could be spirits that protect or guide you.

Page 176, panel 4: Dogeza
The deepest, most formal type of bow. Kyoko often uses it to express her regret and contrition when she feels words are inadequate.

BRING HER OUT NOW.

Wh-Wh-Wh-Why do things happen out of oordeer?!

OH NOOOOOO?! ← Optional →

W-W-We're in for a real storrm!

End of Act 90

...ALL RIGHT...

IT'S...

sigh

...IS ABOUT...

...THE ANGER...

...NOW...

...BUT...

...THAT'S PENT-UP...

...TO EX-PLODE...

...I HOPE THERE'S NOTHING ELSE YOU'RE HIDING FROM ME.

URK!

clench

.....

SORRY!...

OH...

I HEARD ABOUT IT FROM MR. YASHIRO.

REN...

ah hah

.....

...WAS REALLY REALLY WORRIED THAT SOMETHING WAS HAPPENING, BECAUSE YOU SOUNDED STRANGE ON THE PHONE.

!!!

S-SO...

URK!

...

Mr. Yashiro's room is next door.

I'LL DRINK THIS QUICK AND GET OUT OF HERE.

But... I must be considerate...

WELL...!

......

gulp

......

.....

He's not the type to tell someone to leave right after the errand* is done...

That's Ren...

CHEERS!

* To bring Kyoko to his room.

...SEEMED TO HAVE HAPPENED TODAY...

A LOT OF THINGS...

huh?

YES ...?

MS. MOGA-MI...

...WHAT HE SAID!

...SO DON'T WORRY.

...BELIEVE...

Oh no! She looks even worse!

It's not possible...

You can't train a warped Beagle...

mumble mumble mumble

And... in just ten minutes...

SKUTAROO!!

HOW COULD HE HAVE SETTLED THINGS WITH THAT BEAGLE?!

Ten minutes? Beagle? Train?

KYOKO... IS HAVING PROBLEMS TRAINING A DOG?

...

He'll... come again ...for sure...

GIRLS... ...ONLY?!

G...

SQUEE SQUEE

The male crew still has work to do.

Good job!

IT'S ALL GIRLS HERE...

The actors already went to the "good place" they'd checked out beforehand.

Vroo—m

......

KYOKO.

......

HE WON'T TALK ABOUT WHAT HAPPENED TODAY...

I SETTLED THINGS WITH THAT GUY.

I...

...I JUST CAN'T...

N... no...

Blue-Green!

WH-WHAT'S WRONG?! YOU LOOK...

....

...BUT EVERYONE THERE KNOWS THAT "SOMEONE" CAME TO SEE ME...

I WISH I COULD HIDE THE FACT THAT A STALKER WAS AFTER ME...

clock

tmp

...ABOUT WHAT HAD ACTUALLY HAPPENED.

THEN I WENT MISSING, SO THERE'S NO WAY I COULD LIE ABOUT IT...

Blah Blah Blah Blah

Good Job!

Good Job!

I disappeared, then came back all disheveled...

KYOKO.

HUH?

LET'S GET ON TOGETHER.

tmp tmp

Actresses get on first, please!

squee squee

OH...

They said they'll take us back to the hotel by bus...

Director Ogata is so nice. ♡

ESPECIALLY TODAY.

DRIVING TAKES TWICE AS LONG AS WALKING, BUT IT'S DANGEROUS OUT AT NIGHT.

...THAT YOU ONLY KNOW THAT HE WASN'T A CELEBRITY.

...TELL THEM YOU DON'T KNOW WHO IT WAS...

...IF SOMEONE ASKS YOU ABOUT IT...

...AND...

RIGHT.

...SEVERAL CREW MEMBERS WHO CAME LOOKING FOR ME.

DIRECTOR...

...OGATA...

IF THE MEDIA FINDS OUT WHO THE STALKER WAS... IT WILL MAKE GOOD FODDER FOR GOSSIP...

SO PLEASE...

hee hee

I fell unconscious out of sight.

...WHAT REALLY HAPPENED.

EVEN...

...TO THE CREW...

...I DON'T KNOW...

...I SMILED AND LIED THROUGH MY TEETH...

No.

I SHOULDN'T HAVE GONE TO GET YOU IN THE FIRST PLACE!

I'M SOOOOORRY KYOOOOOKO! I SHOULD'VE STOPPED HIM!

um...

NO... IT'S ALL RIGHT.

Skip·Beat!

Act 90: Suddenly, a Love Story
—✳Repeat—

End of Act 89

...THAT YOU RULE NOW.

AS A RESULT, I'LL EVENTU-ALLY...

...TAKE OVER THE PORTION OF HER HEART...

...SHE WAS UNAPPROACH-ABLE...

THIS IS HER FUTURE.

THAT IS WHY...

SHE WAS SO...

THE COILS OF HER EXTRA-ORDINARY SOUL AND AURA.

...ALLUR-ING AND MAJES-TIC...

WHEN KYOKO GOT ALL WORKED UP ABOUT YOU...

...I WANTED YOU TO SEE IT TOO.

...IT WAS SO INTENSE...

UM...

I CAN'T FIND MY TARGET.

HMM?

YES?

...MS. MOMOSE.

Excuse me.

...WE DON'T REALLY KNOW WHAT HAPPENED...

....

....

UH...

DO YOU KNOW WHERE KYOKO IS?

...SOME-THING HAPPEN?

...

DID ...

MAYBE...

WH-WHAT?

Why're you silent?

... ACTU-ALLY ...

...SOME-THING DID HAPPEN?!

WELL!!

DASH DASH DASH DASH DASH

I'M SORRY FOR TROUBLING YOU...

THANK YOU.

...TAKE CARE OF THINGS FOR ME...

PLEASE!!

HE...

I WONDER WHAT...

...HE WAS WORRIED ABOUT. HE LOOKED SO SERIOUS.

EVERYONE HERE LOOKS FINE...

WELL...I UNDERSTOOD WHAT HE WAS TALKING ABOUT EVEN WITHOUT HAVING TO ASK HIM.

Does he really believe he's hiding it from me?

He's so green.

Heh.

...LOOKED SO RELIEVED, IT WAS OBVIOUS WHAT HE WAS WORRIED ABOUT.

...Because I knew I couldn't joke about it this time.

I didn't ask him on purpose...

143

Otherwise he's way too early!

heh heh ah ha ha

I-I see...

...SO I CAME HERE EARLY.

WELL... I HAD SOME BUSINESS...

ISN'T MR. TSURUGA... ARRIVING TOMORROW?

Huh?

Wha...

M-MR. TSURUGA'S MANAGER?!

BUT ACTU-ALLY...

...I'M HERE WITHOUT KNOWING WHY...

s.ig/...

ARE YOU RUNNING AWAY?

Where are you going?

HEY YOU! HOLD IT!

URK

!!

!!

KYOKO WAS ADAMANT THAT SHE'D RATHER PROTECT THE IMAGE OF HER ROLE THAN HERSELF.

....

SO...

?

...BE SATISFIED WITH YOU OCCASION-ALLY CRYING YOUR-SELF TO SLEEP.

I CAN'T...

......

BUT...

The first time in his life he's ever been called a fool!

PO·INT

AND THIS fool!

...

POINT

Huh?!

...be-cause of THIS fool!

clench

YOU'RE STILL A NO-NAME! WHAT DO YOU HAVE TO PROTECT?!

...ARE YOU STUPID?! YOU'RE FALLING INTO HIS TRAP!

shake shake shake

F-FUWA...

.....

SO WHAT IF YOUR IMAGE GETS RUINED?!

...I...

NO...

NO...

JUST USE IT TO SELL YOUR NAME!

A...

.....

...DON'T WANT ...MY IMAGE TARNISHED...

HEY... JUST LOOK AT YOUR-SELF...

You just said that you couldn't even kiss me!

...I WASN'T RAPED!

I...

YOU'LL LOOK LIKE YOU'RE LYING IF YOU INSIST NOTHING HAPPENED.

Her zipper is down. Her stockings are torn.

..."THE WOMAN REINO RAPED"...

KYOKO WILL BE-COME...

TAB-LOIDS ARE LIKE THAT.

...EVEN IF SHE ACTUALLY WASN'T...

WHA...

THEY WRITE ARTICLES SO THE MAGAZINES SELL. THE FACTS DON'T MATTER.

WHEN THE PUBLIC READS IT..."

KYOKO?!

Using her first name?!

Until just now... ...you didn't even use my last name!

Until yesterday... ...you didn't even use her last name!

I COULDN'T EVEN KISS KYOKO.

?!

I DON'T CARE.

I DON'T KNOW WHAT CRIME I'LL BE CHARGED WITH...

...BUT THE GOSSIP WILL BENEFIT US BOTH.

"...RAPED BY VIE GHOUL FRONTMAN REINO IN BROAD DAYLIGHT."

WELL...

...KYOKO'S STILL A NO-NAME, SO THE TABLOIDS WILL REPORT IT LIKE THIS.

"MIO, THE DARK MOON DAUGHTER OF A MILLIONAIRE...

!!

THE HERO ALWAYS...

...GETS IN THE WAY.

...THE HERO LOOKS MORE EVIL THAN I DO.

EVEN IF...

End of Act 88

LIKE YOU WERE JUST NOW...

...PASSIONATE...

...TOWARD ME TOO.

...YOU...

...WILL BE...

...I'LL DO EVERYTHING I CAN...

SO...

...THAN FUWA...

?!

...TO BE MORE...

...MERCILESS...

...THIS GUUUUUUUUUUUUY!

Did... he say he'll stop?! Like it was nothing?!

THIS...

GRRGRR

I... finally made it down here.

where where?!

...

really really reeeeaaaaally

He butted in and gave Shotaro a hard time before I could do the same!

HE'S REALLY TREATING THIS LIKE A CHEAP GAME!

I HAVE NO INTENTION OF TAKING FUWA AWAY FROM YOU.

...DON'T HAVE TO TRY SO HARD TO INSIST THAT HE'S YOURS.

I've got no passion or drive toward Fuwa like you do.

OKAY, I'LL STOP BULLYING FUWA.

blasé

Wha!!

← She picked a fight with all her might, but he simply ignored it.

?

F-FUWA?

I'LL STOP HARASSING FUWA.

STARTING TODAY...

...

I'VE MADE UP MIND...

EVEN IF YOU PRETEND TO HATE HIM...

LOOK AT YOUR HATE WAVES ...

...HAVE ANY-THING LIKE THAT.

AND OUR MEMBERS WANTED TO RISE TO THE TOP OF A MAJOR LABEL IN ONE LEAP.

AS FOR ME...

THE COM-PANY...

I DON'T CARE ABOUT MAJOR LABEL DEALS...

IT...

...JUST WANTED MUSICIANS WHO COULD BEAT FUWA.

....

A GRUDGE?

heh

NO...

...WE DON'T ...

...CAN'T FOR-GIVE?

...THAT YOU JUST...

...WOUND.

A MUCH ...

... HAVE A GRUDGE ...

... AGAINST HIM...

... DEEPER ...

GRAB

?!

...WAS RECORDING?!

NOPE...

...DIDN'T...

...SIMPLY...

COPY...

...STEAL THE SONG SHOTARO...

DID THEY...

heh

IF HE DIDN'T WANT IT STOLEN...

stroke

HE LET US STEAL HIS SONG...

IT'S HIS FAULT.

...HE SHOULDN'T HAVE SPENT SO MUCH TIME FUSSING OVER IT...

......

I...

...THOUGHT...

I CAN'T BE-LIEVE...

...OF SHO-TARO...

...I'D THINK TO ASK...

NO...

Skip·Beat!

Act 88: Suddenly, a Love Story
–Refrain, Part 2–

TK-THUMP...

End of Act 87

IN ANY CASE...

UM... I'M NOT TALKING ABOUT YOUR LIFE...

He has nothing to do with it!!

My Life beLONGS TO ME!

HE...

I'M NOT THE HOUSEMAID WHO SACRIFICED EVERYTHING FOR HIM ANYMORE!

...I DON'T BELONG TO HIM!

Why bring that up?

...DOESN'T SEEM TO THINK SO...

!!!

I'VE...

WHAT'S IMPORTANT IS THAT...

I DON'T CARE WHAT FUWA THINKS OF YOU.

RIGHT.

I DON'T CARE WHAT HE THINKS OF ME!

WHEEZE

WHEEZE

WHEEZE

WHEEZE

...

...

...

WHEEZE

WHEEZE

WHEEZE

::KYOKO...

:KYOKO...

...WHERE'S...

WHA...

um...

......

....

WHEEZE WHEEZE WHEEZE

...WHERE'S...

You want some tea?

ARE YOU ALL RIGHT?

A—

....

THAT FOOL!

THAT'S WHY I TOLD HER TO STAY PUT!

Wheeze

Wheeze

WELL... UH... SHE'S NOT HERE...

...SHE WENT OUT BECAUSE SOMEONE CAME TO SEE HER...

ACCORDING TO SOMEONE WHO OVERHEARD...

!!

YOU'RE FRIENDS WITH SHO FUWA **AND** VIE GHOUL!

Maybe you know all the visual-kei guys?

ExCited

UH...

I'm impressed, Kyoko!

...HIM!

Mio used this poor doll to relieve her stress in the drama.

SHO?

HIS VOICE, THE WAY HE SINGS, AND HIS LOOKS.

DOESN'T HE REMIND YOU OF SHO FUWA A BIT?

REINO ...NOW THAT I THINK ABOUT IT...

YEAH.

I THOUGHT SO TOO.

They're a bit alike.

BUT REINO IS MYSTER- IOUSLY BEAUTIFUL, WHILE SHO'S...

HEY...

GRAB

! / ...

I WAS WRITING A SONG.

THAT WAS AN INTERESTING REMARK...

... / ...

You woke up all by yourself? How?

I ALWAYS HAVE TO PLEAD AND DRAG YOU OUT OF BED. AND THEN YOU SLEEP ON THE FLOOR.

I NEVER WENT TO SLEEP.

...NOT A BIG DEAL...

I ALWAYS HAVE A FEW SONGS IN STOCK.

um...

WELL.

IT'S ALMOST...

SHO.

HOW'S ...THE NEW SONG...

...COMING ALONG?

......

WHAT?!

Almost?!

SO I JUST NEED TO POLISH THEM UP.

WHOA.

IT'S...

WOW!

YEAH.

DONE?! All three songs?!

GEEZ, DIRECTOR OGATA IS WAY TOO CONSIDERATE!

AND HE'S GONE NOW!

PLEASE LEAVE THAT DORK ALONE!

HOW CAN YOU BE SO NICE TO HIM?!

...WHAT SHOULD WE DO ABOUT FUWA'S LUNCH?

I haven't ordered one for him...

"HAPPENED TO SEE ...THIS MORNING?"

...

I've never seen a location shoot before.

I HAPPENED TO SEE KYOKO THIS MORNING AND FOLLOWED HER.

...JUST NEEDED A BREATHER.

I...

No, I didn't.

scuff

HEY...

...

WHERE DID YOU SEE HER?

I hope you didn't bother anybody.

...WHY WERE YOU THERE?

crunch crunch

crunch crunch crunch

SORRY, SINCE YOU'RE ALL READY...

...BUT WE'RE BREAKING FOR LUNCH FIRST.

YES?

AND HE WOULDN'T ASK THE LOCALS TO FIND OUT WHERE THE LOCATION IS.

IF HE GOT **HERE** WITHOUT KNOWING ANYTHING, HE'S GOT ESP.

OH.

oh!

OKAY.

SURE.

tmp tmp tmp

BUT...

DIRECTOR OGATA IS TOO CONSIDERATE...

And I find that cute.

NO, IT'S ALL RIGHT.

I'M SORRY...

When your make-up's all done...

KYOKO.

...UNEASY FOR A MOMENT...

...THAT...

...I...

...FELT...

...HE...

THEY'D ALL BE RAISING A FUSS THAT THEY'D MET VIE GHOUL.

THERE'S NO WAY THAT MAN ASKED OUR CREW EITHER.

fwish

HE PROBABLY DOESN'T KNOW ABOUT THIS LOCATION SHOOT.

THAT CAN'T HAP-PEN.

Sheesh... it's all because of the way Shotaro said that.

...MIGHT COME HERE...

clip clop

clip clop

DON'T...

...AWAY FROM THE SET.

...GO WANDER-ING OFF ALONE...

HE...

...SAID THAT...

...SO SERIOUSLY...

Thank you for reading this volume of *Skip•Beat* this time around, too. I'm saying hello here because...I couldn't fill the sidebars...(*tears*) And the reason is that I was drawing the cover and back flap illustrations, which the Ren x Kyoko readers don't care at all about...(*sweat*) Ugh... ◊◊ 'Cuz...I wanted to draw it...!! ◊◊ In color...! Vampire Hunter Sho...!! And Reino's official portrait...!...When *Hana to Yume* magazine held a character contest for *Skip•Beat*, I drew a pic of Reino, but back then, I hadn't decided what color Reino's hair was. I hesitated, hesitated, hesitated, and in the end, didn't like what I drew...(*wry smile*)...so...I wanted to officially publicize it after I decided to go with my initial image...well well...for people who are fans of Ren or Sho, they probably don't care about this guy at all...

I just went with what I wanted to draw for this volume cover.

To all the Ren fans...I'm sorry (humble apology).

Skip·Beat!

Act 87: Suddenly, a Love Story
–Refrain, Part 1–

...WON'T COME HERE...

...SO HE...

...DOESN'T KNOW WHERE THE SET IS...

...I RETURN...

YEAH, SORRY.

WE WERE REALLY WORRIED!

YEAH, YEAH I GET IT.

...BE-FORE...

tmp

!

PLEASE DON'T DISAPPEAR WITHOUT TELLING ANYBODY.

End of Act 86

ALL RIGHT.

......

...YOU'LL INCONVENIENCE EVERYBODY IF YOU WORK HERE.

All right?

FLASH

Anywhere except HERE, huh?

LISTEN...

I'm sorry Kyoko...

Yes, really.

I'LL LEAVE FOR NOW...

I WANT TO GET MY GUITAR FROM THE STUDIO TOO...

Although I'm used to it now.

...

IF YOU DON'T WANT TO WORK IN THE STUDIO...

...DO IT AT THE HOTEL. PLEASE!

WHAT?

...

stare

Trying to lighten up the gloomy atmosphere somehow...

Is that so...

The mansion we've rented for the location is gorgeous...

He was acting strange last night, so I imagined something outrageous happening...

OH DEAR. I CAN'T BELIEVE HE WAS REALLY HERE...

DON'T...

...THAT I'D HEARD ABOUT THE LOCATION SCENE FROM KYOKO...

I'M GLAD...

OH...

OH?

WHAT? NO BREAKS FOR REN?

Yeah.

REMEMBER HE LOOKED REALLY SERIOUS LAST NIGHT?

YEAH.
When he was on the phone.

chee~ chee~

mrr mrr mrr mrr mrr

HUH?

WHERE TO?

I'M GO-ING.

shrug

clip clop clip clop

clip

TO SEE LITTLE RED RIDING HOOD.

I don't get it.

YOU'RE ALREADY RECORDING A SONG, RIGHT?

WHY'RE YOU WRITING IT NOW?

......

IT'S NONE OF YOUR BUSI-NESS!

WHAT DO YOU MEAN, A NEW SONG?

...THAN STEALING HIS SONG...

...AND FUWA'S MANAGER AND STAFF ARE LOOKING FOR HIM.

Huh?!

WHAT THE HECK.

THERE'S A BETTER WAY TO HURT FUWA...

REINO?

Siga...

WHAT ARE YOU DOING...

Don't you have recording to do?! Stop loafing off here and get back to work!

...HERE?

I'M WORKING.

...

I'M NOT GOOFING OFF.

I'm supposed to be like this!

...LOOK EXTREMELY EVIL... I almost didn't recognize you...

Don't say it with a straight face! Sheesh!

.....

KYOKO...

Y O U...

WE GOT A REPORT FROM THE SPY IN FUWA'S CREW.

IS HE SERIOUS?

A NEW SONG?

HUH?

YEAH.

SO FUWA'S MANAGER HAS ASKED FOR A LITTLE MORE TIME.

WOOD STICK

AND HE SEEMS TO KNOW EXACTLY WHAT YOU LIKE, KYOKO.

It's not as if he just dropped by!

He! Came for a completely meaningless errand!

I heard from the crew...

...THE OTHER DAY, MR. FUWA CAME TO SEE YOU EARLY IN THE MORNING...

Tha— That's be-cause!

Mio's scar is done. Please do her hair and makeup!

HE'S WHAT YOU'D CALL A CHILDHOOD FRIEND.

WHAT?

OH...

Although I wish he wasn't.

IF YOU GROW UP TOGETHER, OF COURSE YOU KNOW!

...BUT MR. FUWA...

HUH?

THEN ...MR. FUWA...

HMM...

"MR"?

KYOKO, YOU WERE IN THE MAKEUP TRAILER, SO I DON'T THINK YOU KNOW...

...CAME TO SEE YOU?

She'll be eighteen in November. She's older than him.

HE'S SEVENTEEN. HE'S THE SAME AGE AS MS. MOMOSE.

Maybe she thinks he's older than she is?

Where?! Where are they?!

Nervous

hide hide

Even I wouldn't usually eat here.

NO WAY, MAN. THOSE SICKLY GUYS WOULDN'T EAT IN A ROOM WITH ORDINARY GUESTS...

THE BEAGLES ARE HERE.

Just eat quickly.

WHAAAAT?!

SHLOOM

DARK MOON staff

S-So those two are...

Oh no!

Look! It's Sho Fuwa! And he's having breakfast with Kyoko!

G—

She hides behind him.

whisper

...GO-ING OUT?

Why "So those two are... REALLY GOING OUT"?!

UH...

...BE-CAUSE...

She was putting on her Mio → makeup.

She came to change. →

WH-WHY DOES EVERY-ONE ASK ME THAT?

.....

COLLAPSE

HUH?

WHAT? ......

....

UH ...

YEAH.

Are you?

Y-You're Leaving?

UH...

WELL ....

UM...

WHAT ABOUT THE NEW SONG?!

W H A A A A T ?!

I'M GOING TO BED. Good night.

tomp tomp

You're really going to bed?!

IS...

...he okay?

WHAT ...

ka-chak

SH-SHO!

OH... DEAR... I CAN'T SIT STILL NOWADAYS...

I'VE GOT TOO MANY THINGS TO WORRY ABOUT...

sigh~

crk crk

shh shh

SHE'S SPECIAL...

SNAP!?

IF THE CD'S GOING TO DROP ON SCHEDULE, HE HAS TO START NOW...

URK

crk

crk

SHO SAYS HE'S GONNA WRITE A NEW SONG.

BUT HE HASN'T STARTED YET...

?!

...SHO...

HEY...

SHO!

kissh

THEN
...

NNH
...

loll loll

IF YOU'RE GOING TO BED, GO BACK TO YOUR OWN ROOM.

WHEN I CAME OUT OF THE BATH, YOU AND VIE GHOUL WERE GLARING AT EACH OTHER.

YOU REALLY SCARED ME.

sigh!!

...

...IT'S ALL RIGHT
...

..... Um...

...Mr. Tsuruga?

...really...

...happened today?

NO...

...NOTH- ING...

N O T H I N G ...

......

AL-THOUGH...

heh heh

...I SHOULDN'T ACT SO SUPERIOR.

I'LL MAKE SURE THINGS GO ACCORDING TO SCHEDULE SO YOU CAN JOIN US ANYTIME!

hee

...YOU'RE WORRYING TOO MUCH.

MR. TSURU-GA...

...did...

I'M REALLY DOING FINE. PLEASE TRUST ME.

KYOKO IS REALLY FRIENDS WITH MR. TSURU-GA...

SHE'S HAV-ING FUN.

HELLO.

Blah Blah Blah Blah

......

Mr. Tsuruga...

WHAT'S THE MATTER?

YOU'RE THERE.

IT'S YOU, ISN'T IT?

MS. MOGAMI?

YES?

....

....

Skip·Beat!

Act 86: Suddenly, a Love Story
−Section B, Part 4−

...I'M...

...SCARED...

End of Act 85

WHILE YOU WERE OUT, YOUR CELL PHONE KEPT RINGING.

WHA...?

Y-YES?

!!!

PEEK

OH.

HEY, KYOKO.

flip

Call Received

Missed Call
Rang for 0 min, 22 sec
No Caller ID

beep

No Caller ID

...MY BRAIN AND MY BODY...

...JUST...

WHEN HE...

...LOOKED RIGHT AT ME...

...COULDN'T I... DO ANYTHING?!

...FROZE UP...

...AND...

...WHEN HE TOUCHED ME...

...FUWA'S OR NOT...

...WHETHER SHE'S...

DOESN'T MATTER...

IT...

mumble

heh

...SPECIAL...

SHE'S...

SHOKO, I'M LEAVING NOW!

oh.

SEE YOU!

Fwooooo

.....

!!!

Oh.

WAH!

shock!

SHE'S THE ANGEL WHO DUPED EVERY-ONE!

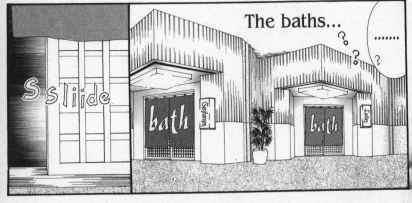

He's....

... He's cooooo wo oooooooooow! What an evil thing to say!

He's discharging his evil drugs!

He is TRULY evil!

...

...AND BLEED HIM DRY...

THEY MUST HAVE MENTAL AND PHYSICAL PROBLEMS...

Yeah... they look all kinds of infected...

WHAT THE...? ARE THEY ALL SICK?

.....

Let's go, Reino. We should go discuss things with the president.

Yeah...

perk

!

...GLARING AT ME...

HE'S...

PISSES ME OFF...

16

......

BEA...

POP!

...

...

IT'S FUWA.

BWA HA HA HA HA!!

JOLT!

?!

?!

HEY! DOES SHO FUWA HAVE THE RIGHT TO LAUGH LIKE THAT?!

He's all scrunched up with laughter.

PROBABLY...!

....

...GOING ON? IS HE... REALLY MAKING FUN OF US...?

....

Look at him! He's jig-gling his legs too!

haw haw haw!

haw!

GRRR

WHAT'S...

SHAKE SHAKE

...SO I THOUGHT I UNDER-STOOD HIM...

BECAUSE...

...I THOUGHT HE WASN'T WORRIED...

BUT...

...HE SEEMED OKAY...

...ACTING LIKE NORMAL...

...THAT HE WASN'T OKAY...

...RE-CENTLY...

THUD

... FOR THE FIRST TIME, I REAL-IZED...

ACTU-ALLY...

...EVEN WOMEN CAN'T HELP STARING AT YOU.

SHOKO... YOU'VE GOT SUCH A GOOD FIGURE...

UM...

?

Oh ...

... thanks. ♡

WHAT?!

My college has a drama school that a lot of celebrities graduated from.

I WANTED TO BE AN ACTRESS WHEN I WAS IN COLLEGE.

LIKE, "WHY DON'T YOU QUIT BEING A MANAGER AND BECOME A MODEL INSTEAD?"

DON'T PEOPLE SCOUT YOU SOME-TIMES?

TO TELL THE TRUTH... I THINK I'M BETTER AT JUDGING OTHER PEOPLE'S TALENTS AND SUPPORTING THEM.

...AND NOW I'M A MANA-GER...

BUT I COULDN'T COMPLETELY GIVE IT UP... I WANTED TO WORK IN SHOWBIZ SOMEHOW...

That's too bad.

REALLY?

BUT I REALIZED I DIDN'T HAVE THE TALENT, SO I GAVE UP MY STUDIES AND MY DREAM.

I'VE ALWAYS WATCHED HIM...

heh

YES. AND I WANT TO CONGRAT-ULATE MYSELF FOR THAT DECI-SION.

YOU DECIDED THAT YOU DIDN'T HAVE THE TALENT?

yay yay

Whee!

Yaaay! ♡

I HAVEN'T BEEN IN A PUBLIC BATH FOR A WHILE!

MS. MOMOSE SHOULD'VE COME TOO!

I'LL BE EMBARRASSED IF OTHER PEOPLE ARE THERE, SO I'LL USE THE BATH IN OUR ROOM.

um

Sorry.

^-^

EMBARRASSED?

She's used to it, since she grew up in a Japanese inn.

I DON'T MIND IF STRANGERS SEE ME NAKED. WE'LL PROBABLY NEVER SEE EACH OTHER AGAIN ANYWAY...

And they're women too.

hmm

THEN IT MIGHT ACTUALLY BE EMBARRASSING...

OR DO PEOPLE STARE AT YOU WHEN YOU'RE A CELEBRITY?

Skip·Beat!☆

Act 85: Suddenly, a Love Story
–Section B, Part 3–

Skip·Beat!

Volume 15

CONTENTS

Skip·Beat!

15

Story & Art by Yoshiki Nakamura

Skip·Beat!